IAN FITZGERA

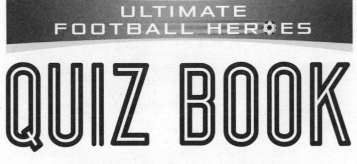

ULTIMATE
FOOTBALL HEROES

QUIZ BOOK

ARE YOU A FOOTBALL SUPER FAN?

DINO

First published by Dino Books in 2020,
An imprint of Bonnier Books UK,
The Plaza,
535 Kings Road,
London SW10 0SZ

@dinobooks
@footieheroesbks
www.heroesfootball.com
www.bonnierbooks.co.uk

© Studio Press 2020

Design by www.envydesign.co.uk

Paperback ISBN: 9781789463309

British Library cataloguing-in-publication data:
A catalogue record for this book is available from the British Library.

Printed and bound in Great Britain by Clays Lltd, Elcograf S.p.A.

1 3 5 7 9 10 8 6 4 2

MIX
Paper from
responsible sources
FSC® C018072

ACKNOWLEDGEMENTS

I would like to thank Laura Pollard at Bonnier Books for
giving me the opportunity to create this book, and for her
expert coaching. Pep Guardiola couldn't have done it better.
Much thanks also to Sophie Blackman at Bonnier for seeing
me through to the final whistle. I would also like to show my
appreciation to Rob Ward for designing the pages and helping it
all hang together properly.

I'm also extremely grateful for the proofreading skills of
Geoff West – a great shot-stopper who also pulled of a few great
saves!

Finally, of course, I am indebted to Matt and Tom Oldfield,
writers of the brilliant Ultimate Football Heroes series, without
whose efforts this book would not have been possible.

Ian Fitzgerald
London
2020

TABLE OF CONTENTS

INTRODUCTION

You love football, right? But how much do you know about it? Not just *know* but *really know*?

This book is going to test your expertise on what for many is the greatest international soccer competition there is: the Euros. OK, there's the World Cup, but (and say it softly), it's a tournament than sometimes gets a little bit boring. The Euros is where the real action is. The games are more competitive, the quality of football is higher, and it's just a lot more fun!

And fun is what you'll have racking your brains to answer the 50 quizzes waiting for you in the pages that follow. There are all sorts of questions to tackle, from multiple choice, to anagrams, word puzzles, true or false, code-breaking and much, much more. We've jumbled things up to create a mix of Easy, Medium, and Hard quizzes – all clearly flagged.

We start with England's qualification campaign for the 2020 Euros and then we'll move on to the group stages of every tournament since 1960, from teams as diverse as Germany, France, Italy and Spain, to Azerbaijan, Luxembourg, Hungary and San Marino. Then it's on to the Last 16, the quarter-finals, the semi-finals and the finals of the most exciting Euros tournaments in history. We don't expect you to know all the answers, which is why we've included them at the end of the book. Don't cheat, though: working out the things you don't know is half the enjoyment!

So, are you ready for kick-off? Come on, let's play!

SECTION 1

THE QUALIFIERS

ENGLAND'S 2020 EURO QUALIFICATION CAMPAIGN

Difficulty rating: Medium ⚽ ⚽

Let's start our travels through European football with these brainteasers about England's journey to the 2020 Euros.

1) What was England's group in the qualifiers for Euro 2020: A, B, C, D or E?

2) Match up the capital cities to the other countries in England's qualification group:

Country	Capital
Czech Republic	Sofia
Bulgaria	Pristina
Montenegro	Prague
Kosovo	Podgorica

3) Which English player scored two hat-tricks in qualification?

4) England lost just one game in qualification – to which team?

5) How many Harrys played for England during the 2020 Euro qualifications? Give their full names!

6) Name the two England squad members who play for non-English clubs. Which clubs do they play for?

7) Who scored his first-ever England goal in injury time in the 4–0 away win to Kosovo?

8) Which team supplied the most players for England's qualification squad?

9) Name those players!

10) England played three of its four home qualification games at Wembley. Where did it play the remaining game?

11) 'NEXT NARRATED LAND ROLE' is an anagram of which England player's name?

12) Which England player scored in every qualification game?

YOUNG GUNS!

Difficulty rating: Hard ⚽ ⚽ ⚽

The Euro qualifiers over the years have seen some exciting new talents emerge. Here are the young lads who've done great!

1) Aged just fifteen years and 300 days in 2016, Martin Ødegaard is the youngest-ever player (so far) to appear in a Euro qualifying game – for which national team?

2) The Netherlands' nineteen-year-old P_ _ _ _ _ _ K_ _ _ _ _ _ _ scored his first international goal in a 2005 Euro Qualifier against Malta.

3) In 1963, this twenty-one-year-old England defender and future captain (initials: B.M.) played in a 6–3 two-legged qualifier loss to France.

4) Wales's twenty-one-year-old Daniel James scored on his first international competitive start against which team: Slovenia or Slovakia?

5) Unscramble 'EG FACES CRAB' to discover the twenty-one-year-old midfielder who helped Spain qualify for Euro 2008.

6) Northern Ireland's greatest-ever player (initials: G.B.) was twenty in October 1966 when he made his Euro qualifying debut in a 2–0 loss to England.

7) Seventeen-year-old Gareth Bale scored for Wales on his Euro qualifying debut in 2006. True or false?

8) Which Belgian powerhouse striker (initials: R.L.) was seventeen years and 113 days when he made his Euro qualifying debut in 2010?

9) This player called Johan was nineteen when he scored on his international debut for The Netherlands in a 1966 Euro qualifier. What was his surname?

10) This French superstar was nineteen when he scored his hundredth career goal, in a 4–0 Euro 2020 qualifier over Andorra.

RECORD BREAKERS

Difficulty rating: Hard ⚽ ⚽ ⚽

Lots of records have been broken in Euro qualification matches. Can you solve these puzzles about European record breakers?

1) He's Portuguese, he likes to look good, and he's scored more goals in Euro qualifiers than anyone else. Who is he?

2) And how many times has he netted?

   a) 22   b) 27   c) 31

3) Two players have each scored thirteen times in qualifying. One is Northern Irish; the other is Polish. Their names, please.

4) Can you name the only team, despite repeated attempts, that has failed to get past the qualification stage since 1964?

5) Three players have scored five goals in a single qualifying game. Hungary's Tibor Nyilasi is one. The other two were England's 'Supermac' in 1975 and Holland's 'MvB' in 1990. What are their real names?

6) Who beat San Marino 13–0 in a 2006 qualifying game, the biggest victory in Euro history?

7) This Italian goalie kept a clean sheet for 644 minutes in 2010–11, the longest consecutive run in Euro qualification. Who is he?

8) Another Italian 'keeper is the oldest-ever player to take part in qualification. He was forty-one years and 90 days when his country played Sweden in May 1983. His initials are D.Z. What's his name?

9) Which team has the highest number of successful qualifications in a row?

10) And how many?

a) Five   b) Six   c) Seven

DEWCH YMLAEN, CYMRU!

Difficulty rating: Medium ⚽ ⚽

That's 'Come on, Wales' in plain English. Here's a look at the boyos' eventful 2020 qualification campaign.

1) What is Gareth Bale's nickname at Real Madrid, due to his sporting obsession?:

    a) Mr Darts
    b) The Golfer
    c) Badminton Bale

2) What is the Premiership parent club of rising star Ethan Ampadu?

3) Wales played eight qualifying games for Euro 2020, but with how many wins, draws and losses?

4) Where do Wales play their home matches?

5) Which Wales player's name is an anagram of 'YAMS ON AREA'?

6) Baku is the capital city of which country in Wales's qualifying group?

7) Wales's No. 1 keeper plays for Crystal Palace. What's his name?

8) How many games did manager Ryan Giggs play for Manchester United:

   a) 477   b) 523   c) 672

9) Who captains Wales's qualification group opponents, Croatia?

10) Including the 2020 tournament, how many times has Wales qualified for the Euros?

   a) Once   b) Twice   c) Five times

CRACK THE CODE

Difficulty rating: Easy

Time for some numbers! Don't panic, this one's actually quite easy and lots of fun once you get the hang of it. We've used a simple number code to represent some of England's players for the 2020 qualification campaign.

A = 1, B = 2 and so on until Z = 26.

Once you've done a couple, see if you can guess the names just by looking at the patterns!

1) 5-18-9-3 / 4-9-5-18

2) 18-15-19-19 / 2-1-18-11-12-5-25

3) 1-1-18-15-14 / 23-1-14 / 2-9-19-19-1-11-1

4) 18-1-8-5-5-13 / 19-20-5-18-12-9-14-7

5) 4-5-12-5 / 1-12-12-9

6) 4-5-3-12-1-14 / 18-9-3-5

7) 10-5-19-19-5 / 12-9-14-7-1-18-4

8) 10-15-5 / 7-15-13-5-26

9) 11-9-5-18-1-14 / 20-18-9-16-16-9-5-18

10) 8-1-18-18-25 / 23-9-14-11-19

11) 2-5-14 / 3-8-9-12-23-5-12-12

12) 20-1-13-13-25 / 1-2-18-1-8-1-13

NATIONAL ANTHEMS

Difficulty rating: Medium ⚽ ⚽

Can you identify these countries that England has played in qualification from just their national anthem and one other clue?

1) 'Hen Wlad Fy Nhadau', or 'Land of My Fathers'.
   You cross the Severn Bridge to get here.

2) This team's anthem is called 'Hatikvah'
   (to us it's 'The Hope'). Capital city: Jerusalem.

3) 'El Gran Carlemany', which translates as 'The Great
   Charlemagne'. This tiny country is sandwiched between
   Spain and France: A_ _ _ _ _ A.

4) 'Hýmnos pros tin Eleftherían', or 'Hymn to Liberty'.
   Its islands include Corfu, Crete and Rhodes.

5) You can do the 'Istiklal Marsı' ('Independence March')
   all the way to Istanbul.

6) They sing 'Oj, svijetla majska zoro' ('Oh, Bright Dawn of May') in this country whose name translates as 'Black Mountain'.

7) A country famed for its mountains, chocolate, banks and watches has a national anthem called 'Schweizerpsalm'.

8) This little state between Switzerland and Austria is 'High on the Young Rhine' ('Obem an jungen Rhein'). Anagram: 'HIS NICE NETTLE'.

9) In the fair city of Dublin they sing 'Amhrán na bhFiann' ('The Soldier's Song).

10) Zlatan should know the words to 'Du gamla, du fria' ('Thou Ancient, Thou Free').

2020 STAT ATTACK – FIRST LEG!

Difficulty rating: Hard 🎱 🎱 🎱

You love football stats, right? So, see how many of these 2020 Euro qualification facts and figures you know – or can work out!

1) Which keeper kept the highest number of clean sheets (seven)?

   a) Thibaut Courtois (Belgium)
   b) Fehmi Mert Günok (Turkey)
   c) Guilherme Alvim Marinato (Russia)

2) How many clean sheets did England's Jordan Pickford manage?

3) What was the total attendance for all of the qualification games?

   a) 3,346,279   b) 4,992,085   c) 5,220,354

4) Who was England's leading goal assist provider?

5) How many shots on goal, on average, per game?

   a) 19   b) 27   c) 38

6) What was the percentage of home wins?

   a) 51 per cent   b) 60 per cent   c) 72 per cent

7) And the number of goals per game, on average?

   a) 2.7   b) 3.2   c) 4.1

8) Which team performed worst in the Euro 2020 qualifiers?

   a) Faroe Islands   b) Gibraltar   c) San Marino

9) And how many goals did they score and concede during their ten games?

10) On average, how often was a goal scored?

   a) Every 28 minutes
   b) Every 38 minutes
   c) Every 48 minutes

2020 STAT ATTACK – SECOND LEG!

Difficulty rating: Hard ⚽ ⚽ ⚽

The first round of Stat Attack wasn't enough for you?
Good, here are some more to wrap your brain around.

1) How many teams took part in Euro 2020 qualifying?

2) How many games were played, excluding play-offs?

3) And how many goals were scored in total?:

   a) 623　　　　b) 714　　　　c) 801

4) How many goals were scored in injury time?

   a) 18　　　　b) 43　　　　c) 84

5) Which team had the best pass completion percentage?
   And can you also guess the percentage rate?

   a) Spain　　　b) England　　　c) France

6) Which team enjoyed the highest possession percentage? Can you guess the percentage rate?

   a) Italy   b) Germany   c) Spain

7) Which team had the most attempts on goal? How many?

   a) Belgium   b) Spain   c) France

8) Which team scored the most goals in qualification? How many?

   a) Spain   b) Belgium   c) England

9) Which player top-scored in qualification, and with how many?

   a) Harry Kane   b) Cristiano Ronaldo   c) Teemu Pukki

10) Which hard-working goalie made the most saves? How many?

a) Benjamin Büchel (Liechtenstein)
b) Henry Bonello (Malta)
c) Aram Airapetyan (Armenia)

LINE-UPS

Difficulty rating: Medium ⚽ ⚽

When Scotland played Belgium at Hampden Park in September 2019 (and lost 4–0), there were lots of well-known and British-based players on show. Try to figure out the starting line-ups of both teams based on their clubs. We've included their squad numbers and each player's initials, if that helps.

SCOTLAND

1 Wigan Athletic
(DM)

4 Blackburn Rovers
(CM)

5 Leeds
(LC)

2 Kilmarnock
(SO'D)

3 Liverpool
(AR)

16 Norwich City
(KM)

10 Celtic
(CM)

6 Manchester United
(SM)

20 Celtic
(RC)

19 West Brom
(MP)

17 West Ham
(RS)

BELGIUM

1 Real Madrid
(TC)

3 Vissel Kobe
(TV)

5 Spurs
(JV)

2 Spurs
(TA)

6 Wolves
(LD)

8 Leicester City
(YT)

22 Anderlecht
(NC)

15 PSG
(TM)

7 Manchester City
(KDB)

14 Napoli
(DM)

9 Inter Milan
(RL)

A–Z OF 2020 QUALIFICATION

Difficulty rating: Medium ⚽ ⚽

A quickfire round to end this section. Each answer begins with a different letter of the alphabet. There are twenty-six in total.

A – Country. Capital city, Tirana

B – Daley. Dutch defender

C – CR7

D – German for 'Germany'

E – Spurs and Denmark

F – Łukasz. Sounds wonderful!

G – Chiellini. Scary Italian defender

H – Home of Scottish football

I – Group H country. Capital city Reykjavik

J – Sancho. Dortmund. England

K – Vincent. Belgium. Legend

L – Kevin. Italian defender. Baked pasta?

M – João. Portugal

30

N – Nizhny. Russia plays here

O – Belgium and Liverpool forward

P – 'Poland' in Polish (anagram: SKAPOL)

Q – Win these, reach the finals

R – Koeman. Dutch coach

S – Polish keeper. Hard to spell!

T – City, Latvian capital

U – Samuel. French defender

V – Hamburg stadium

W – Georginio. Dutch midfielder

X – Granit, Swiss midfielder

Y – Zhirkov. Russian midfielder

Z – Gianfranco. Italy and Chelsea

SECTION 2

THE GROUP GAMES

HIGH-SCORING GAMES

Difficulty rating: Hard ⚽ ⚽ ⚽

1) Croatia 2-4 England (2004). Which Liverpool-born striker scored twice?

2) Yugoslavia 3-4 Spain (2000). Which UK club did Spanish goal-scorer Gaizka Mendieta play for?

   a) Newcastle   b) Sunderland   c) Middlesbrough

3) Russia 3–3 Czech Republic (1996). Vladimír Šmicer equalized for the Czechs with how long left on the clock?

   a) 10 minutes   b) 2 minutes   c) 30 seconds

4) Yugoslavia 3–3 Slovenia (2000). The Yugoslavs were…

   a) 0–3 down with 30 minutes left
   b) 0–3 down with 30 minutes left, down to 10 men
   c) 0–3 down with 30 minutes left, down to 10 men,
      goal-line clearance at 3–3

5) Denmark 5–0 Yugoslavia (1984). Where were the 1984 Euros held?

6) Denmark 3–2 Belgium (1984). The Danes' manager Sepp Piontek was from which country?

a) Denmark   b) Germany   c) Sweden

7) Germany 3–2 Netherlands (1980). Which nineteen-year-old came off the bench to earn the first of his record-breaking 150 caps for Germany?

8) Spain 3–2 Denmark (1988). Spain's matchwinner was the left wingback R_F_E_ / G_R_I_L_

9) Netherlands 4–1 France (2008). Kirk Duyt scored for Holland in this convincing victory, true or false?

10) Turkey 3–2 Czech Republic (2008). The Turks were 2–0 down with how long left?

a) 15 minutes   b) 10 minutes   c) 5 minutes

PENALTY!

Difficulty rating: Easy ⊛

There are plenty of penalty incidents to choose from in the Euro group stages. Here's a selection:

1) Whose penalty for France, in the ninety-third minute, beat England 2–1 in 2004?

   a) Zidane   b) Cantona   c) Henry

2) In 2008 who did Hakan Yakin score a penalty for, against Portugal?

   a) Turkey   b) Germany   c) Switzerland

3) When Italy beat France in 2008 'RIP ROAD LANE' notched a penalty. Unscramble his name.

4) Henrik Larsson scored for who against Denmark in 2004?

5) When England beat the Netherlands 4–1 in 1996, whose penalty opened the scoring (Clue: initials AS)?

36

6) Kubilay Türkyilmaz equalized for which country against England in 1996?

   a) Turkey   b) Greece   c) Germany

7) Gary Mc– who scored a penalty for Scotland in their 3–0 win against the CIS in 1992. Complete his surname.

8) And what does the CIS stand for?

   a) Commonwealth of Independent States
   b) Confederation of Irish Soccer
   c) Community of International Superstars

9) He got the winner for Italy against Turkey (2 1) in 2000:
   F_L_P_O / I_Z_G_I

SEEING RED

Difficulty rating: Medium ⚽ ⚽

The Euros only occur every four years, so imagine how this lot feel about getting sent off in the group stages!

1) How many red cards have been dished out since the first tournament in 1960?

   a) 25   b) 35   c) 45

2) Petar Hubchev and Juan Antonio Pizzi was the first double sending off, in 1984. Their respective teams?

3) Sent off against Croatia in 2008, which German's name can be literally translated into English as 'Sebastian Pigwatcher'?

4) Which two Euro tournaments had the most red cards, and how many?

5) Between which tournaments were there no red cards at all?

6) Sokratis Papastathopoulos and Wojciech Szczęsny was the second double sending off, in 2012. Which were their respective national teams?

7)   France's Eric Abidal holds which record, from 2008?

   a) Only red card overturned
   b) Wouldn't leave the pitch
   c) Fastest-ever red card

8)   What percentage of sendings off were straight reds?

   a) 30 per cent   b) 48 per cent   c) 66 per cent

9)   Which 10-minute period of a Euro game, on average,
     has the most sendings off?

   a) 0–10 minutes   b) 11–20 minutes   c) 21–30 minutes
   d) 31–40 minutes   e) 41–50 minutes   f) 51–60 minutes
   g) 61–70 minutes   h) 71–80 minutes   i) 81–90 minutes

10) Manuel Amoros was the first man ever sent off in the
    group stages. Which country did he play for?

11) The only Irish sending off is K_ _ _ H / A _ _ _ _ _ S

12) How many English players have been sent off?

GREAT GROUP GAME GOALS!

Difficulty rating: Medium ⚽ ⚽

Once you've answered these questions about the
most incredible Euro goals, look them up online.
No cheating, though!

1) Which major striker opened the scoring for Sweden versus
   France in 2012 with an incredible scissor kick?

2) This Swede's amazing back-heel lobbed volley made it 1–1
   against Italy in 2004.

3) Which genius Geordie made it 2–0 against Scotland in
   1996 by lifting the ball over the defender with his left, then
   slotting home with his right?

4) L_I_ / F_G_, for Portugal, belted an unstoppable 25-yarder
   past David Seaman in 2000.

5) In 1980, which England midfielder, nicknamed 'The Crab'
   and with the initials R.W., lobbed a Belgian defender then
   chipped the keeper.

6) This French legend's 25-yard free kick screamer helped see off England in 2004.

7) Swede. Against Greece. The year 2008. A 20-yarder. Outside of right boot. Top corner.

8) Which Swede scored a bullet-like flying header in his country's 5–0 win over Bulgaria in 2004? It was voted goal of the tournament.

9) Ronnie executed a perfect flying volley for the Republic of Ireland against the USSR in 1988 – but what's his surname?

10) Another Swede, another goal: T_M_S / B_O_I_ bamboozled England in Euro '92.

LOST IN TRANSLATION

Difficulty rating: Easy

These players' names have all been translated into English.
Can you translate them back into their original language?
We've given you a few clues.

1) Didier 'of the Fields'
   (French: D_S_H_M_S)

2) Dennis 'mountain camp'
   (Dutch: B_R_K_M_)

3) Emmanuel 'little'
   (French: P_T_T)

4) Pep 'guardroom'
   (Spanish: G_A_D_O_A)

5) Luis 'fig'
   (Portuguese: F_G_)

6) Frank 'beef'
   (French: L_B_E_F)

7) Johann 'bird'
   (German: V_G_L)

8) Enrico 'church'
   (Italian: C_I_S_)

9) Raul 'well done!'
   (Spanish: B_A_O)

10) Laurent 'white'
    (French: B_A_C)

11) Fabio 'big'
    (Italian: G_O_S_)

12) Dimitris 'trumpet'
    (Greek: S_L_I_G_D_S)

HAT=TRICK HEROES

Difficulty rating: Medium ⚽ ⚽

It's time to celebrate the players who've scored hat-tricks in the Euro group stages. It's as easy as 1-2-3!

1) Which French captain netted three times in a 5–0 win over Belgium in 1984?

2) Which Frenchman scored a hat-trick in France's 1984 3–2 win over Yugoslavia?

3) Who scored the fastest-ever group stage hat-trick, in just eighteen minutes?

4) The oldest Euro hat-trick scorer was twenty-eight years and 364 days. Who is he?

5) Only one player has scored two hat-tricks in the same tournament. Il s'appelle?

6) Every Euro hat-trick scorer has ended up on the winning side. True or false?

7) David Villa bagged three in the 2008 4–1 win against Russia. Who for?

8) Which UK team did The Netherlands' Marco van Basten score a hat-trick against in 1988?

9) Sérgio Conceição scored for which team in the 3–0 victory against Germany in 2000?

10) And for which team did Klaus Allofs score against The Netherlands in a 3–2 win in 1980?

11) How many hat-tricks have been scored in Euro group games?

a) Six   b) Nine   c) Twelve

12) And how many hat-tricks were scored in the first four tournaments, between 1960 and 1972?

a) None   b) Two   c) Four

TRUE OR FALSE

Difficulty rating: Medium ⚽ ⚽

Here's a bag of 'true or false' questions about the Euro group stages.

1) Taulant (Albania) and Granit Xhaka (Switzerland), in 2016, are the first brothers to play against each other in Euro history.

2) France's Eric Abidal was the fastest sending off, in the twenty-fourth minute against Italy in 2008.

3) Didier Deschamps, at forty-three in 2012, was the youngest coach in Euro history.

4) Giovanni Trapattoni of Italy was the oldest coach, at seventy-three years old, for the Republic of Ireland in 2012.

5) Russia scored the fastest group stage goal in 2004, against Greece, after only four minutes.

6) Austria's Ivica Vastić is the Euro's oldest goalscorer at thirty-seven years old in 2008.

7) Germany's Lothar Matthäus is the Euros' oldest outfield player, being thirty-nine in 2000.

8) Jetro Willems, the youngest player in Euro finals history at eighteen years and 71 days in 2012, hails from Belgium.

9) Germany has the most consecutive progressions from the group stages.

EURO INJURY TIME GOALS

Difficulty rating: Medium ⚽ ⚽

Injury time is often when all the fun happens and when a game's result is decided.

1) How many group stage injury time goals have been scored in Euros history?

   a) 18   b) 34   c) 77

2) And which team has scored the most goals?

   a) Portugal   b) Germany   c) England

3) How many first-half injury time goals have there been in the Euros?

   a) 3   b) 6   c) 9

4) Who is the only player to score two injury time goals in the same Euro game?

   a) Jürgen Klinsmann
   b) Cristiano Ronaldo
   c) Zinedine Zidane

5) Who scored the first-ever group game injury time goal at the Euros?

   a) Jürgen Klinsmann
   b) Cristiano Ronaldo
   c) Zinedine Zidane

6) And in which year's tournament did it take place?

7) The 2016 tournament saw the highest number of injury time goals in the group stages. True or false?

8) England's only ever injury time goal at the Euros was scored by 'ONE OWNER YAY'. Solve this anagram.

9) The latest group game injury time goal in history was scored in what minute in 2016?

   a) 94th   b) 96th   c) 98th

10) Two players share the honour of an injury time goal: a Frenchman D_M_T_I / P_Y_T and a Northern Irishman N_A_L / M_G_N_

MINNOWS

Difficulty rating: Medium ⚽ ⚽

Some teams have never made it past the group stages, so this is your last chance to celebrate some Euro Championship battlers – by guessing who they are!

1) This country reached the group stages in 2016 and its name is an anagram of 'IBALANA'.

2) A northern European country, known for its spectacular fjords, this country's capital city is Oslo. They reached the group stages in 2000.

3) 'U ARE INK'. Unscramble this to find a country, close to Russia, that was in the 2016 group stages.

4) Its capital city is Sofia. Also, Great Uncle B_ _ _ _ _ _ _ is one of the Wombles!

5) Some of this country's league clubs include Rapid Vienna, Sturm Graz and Red Bull Salzburg. They were in the 2008 group stages.

6) This country is next door to northern Italy. They got to the 2020 group stages.

7) This country is sandwiched between Lithuania and Estonia, and its capital is Riga. Its national team made up the numbers in the 2004 group stage.

8) They climbed over Hadrian's Wall and came south to face England in the 1996 group stages.

A–Z OF THE GROUP STAGES

Difficulty rating: Medium ⚽ ⚽

'A' is for… well, you tell us. Work your way through this
alphabet of footballing excellence!

A – Del Piero. Italy. 1996.

B – Germany's capital city.

C – Makélélé. France
midfielder.

D – Bergkamp. Netherlands.

E – Van der Sar. Netherlands
goalie, 2008.

F – F_R_A_D_ Llorente.
Spain, 2012.

G – Milan Baros's club in
Turkey, 2012.

H – Mats 'MUMSHEL'
(anagram). Germany.

I – Bodo I_L_N_R.
Germany keeper. 1992

J – J_L_O_ Lescott. England
defender.

K – Benzema. France.
Real Madrid.

L – Hugo Lloris's French
club in 2012.

M – Gary Neville's old club.

N – Gary and Phil's dad's name!

O – Alex _ _ _ _ _ _ Chamberlain.

P – Sokratis's last name.

Q – Stephen Q_I_N. Ireland. 2016.

R – Mancini. Italy. 1988.

S – Zlatan's country.

T – T_M_S Rosický. Czech Republic.

U – Organisers of the tournament.

V – Jordi Alba's club, 2012. Spain.

W – Theo. England. 2012.

X – Taulent. Albania. Granit's brother.

Y – Djorkaeff. France. 1996.

Z – Boudewijn. The Netherlands. 2000.

53

SECTION 3

THE LAST 16

NAME THAT COUNTRY

Difficulty rating: Easy ⚽

Can you name these 2016 Last 16 countries from these brief descriptions?

1) The fictional character of Tintin comes from here. Capital city: Brussels.

2) 'Buongiorno' means 'hello' in this country.

3) The explorer Vasco da Gama was from here.

4) Where the Alps are. And Lake Geneva.

5) Lyon is this country's second biggest city.

6) Ludwig van Beethoven, composer of nine symphonies, was born in this country.

7) You've probably been to one of its Costas for your holidays.

8) Capital city: Reykjavik.

9) This country's good at rugby, too – and singing.

10) Luka Modrić is from here.

11) Unscramble 'ASK VIOLA' to get this country.

12) Capital city: Budapest.

13) Its national symbol is a White Eagle.

14) The smallest country in the UK. Its capital city is Belfast.

15) Number 14's next-door neighbour.

16) The home of football!

MORE LOST IN TRANSLATION

Difficulty rating: Medium ⚽ ⚽

Here are more names and the languages they're translated from, all from the Last 16 in Euro 2016. Good luck!

1) Yann 'summer'
   (German: S_M_E_)

2) Toni 'duckweed'
   (German: K_O_S)

3) Ciro 'motionless'
   (Italian: I_M_B_L_)

4) Ricardo 'oak'
   (Portuguese: C_R_A_H_)

5) Lucas 'worthy'
   (French: D_G_E)

6) Manuel 'new'
   (German: N_U_R)

7) Graziano 'skin'
   (Italian: P_L_E)

8) Raphael 'warrior'
   (Portuguese: G_E_R_I_O)

9) Luca 'bruises'
   (Croatian: M_D_I_)

10) Lorenzo 'distinguished'
    (Italian: I_S_G_E)

11) Petr 'guild'
    (Czech: Č_C_)

12) Fabian 'free'
    (German F_E_)

RETURN OF THE DREADED NUMBER PUZZLE!

Difficulty rating: Easy (eventually)

Put your maths hat back on. This number puzzle is all about players from the Last 16 round in 2016. Remember, as before, A = 1, B = 2, C = 3, and so on. We've put their country in brackets as a clue.

1) 9-22-1-14 / 18-1-11-9-20-9-3
   (Croatia)

2) 2-9-18-11-9-18 / 2-10-1-18-14-1-19-15-14
   (Iceland)

3) 5-12-9-1-17-21-9-13 / 13-1-14-7-1-12-1
   (France)

4) 2-1-18-20-15-19-26 / 19-1-12-1-13-15-14
   (Poland)

5) 2-18-5-5-12 / 5-13-2-15-12-15
   (Switzerland)

6) 13-1-18-9-15 / 13-1-14-4-26-21-11-9-3
   (Croatia)

7) 22-9-5-9-18-9-14-8-1
   (Portugal)

8) 1-14-4-18-5-1 / 2-1-18-26-1-7-12-9
   (Italy)

9) 2-1-3-1-18-25 / 19-1-7-14-1
   (France)

10) 13-1-18-5-11 / 8-1-13-19-9-11
    (Slovakia)

11) 1-18-9-20-26 / 1-4-21-18-9-26
    (Spain)

12) 13-1-18-3 / 1-14-4-18-5 / 20-5-18 / 19-20-5-7-5-14
    (Germany)

QUIZ 24

SHOW US YOUR BADGE

Difficulty rating: Medium ⚽ ⚽

Identify these well-known Last 16 teams from 2016 by their badges.

1) A black eagle and the words
   'DEUTSCHER FUSSBALL-BUND'

2) A green, white and red shield, and the words
   'ITALIA FIGC'

3) Red shield with a red cross behind it, and the letters
   'F.P.F.'

4) A shield with another shield inside it, a crown, a couple of columns, a football and loads more...

5) A shield with a black, yellow and red stripe, and the words
   'URBSFA KBVB 1895'

6) A white cross on a red background.

7) Three lions!

8) A red dragon.

9) A red-and-white checked shield and the letters 'HNS'.

10) A wavy blue-and-white flag, a football and the letters 'KSI'.

CLUBS AT EURO 2016

Difficulty rating: Medium ⚽ ⚽

All the players at Euro 2016 came from football clubs from all over the world – as you'll find out here.

1) Liverpool and Juventus supplied the most players at Euro 2016. True or false?

2) Spurs sent eleven players who were involved in the Last 16. Can you identify them:

a) H_G_ / L_O_I_ (France)
b) K_L_ / W_L_E_ (England)
c) D_N_Y / R_S_ (England)
d) H_R_Y / K_N_ (England)
e) E_I_ / D_E_ (England)
f) D_L_ / A_L_ (England)
g) B_N / D_V_E_ (Wales)
h) T_B_ / A_D_R_E_R_L_ (Belgium)
i) J_N / V_R_O_G_E_ (Belgium)
j) M_U_A / D_M_E_E (Belgium)

3) Manchester United had a total of ten players in the Last 16. Can you identify them?:

a) A_T_O_Y / M_R_I_L (France)
b) M_R_A_ / S_H_E_D_R_I_ (France)
c) C_R_S / S_A_L_N_ (England)
d) W_Y_E / R_O_E_ (England)
e) M_R_U_ / R_S_F_R_ (England)
f) B_S_I_N / S_H_E_N_T_I_E_ (Germany)
g) P_D_Y / M_N_I_ (Northern Ireland)
h) D_V_D / D_ / G_A (Spain)
i) M_R_U_N_ / F_L_A_N_ (Belgium)
j) M_T_E_ / D_R_I_N (Italy)

4) Only one of the Republic of Ireland's twenty-three-man squad played outside of England, for LA Galaxy. Unscramble the following to reveal his name: 'O, A KNEE BRIBE'.

NAMES AND PLACES

Difficulty rating: Medium

All of these players have last names that are also places. Can you figure them out?

1) Wales defender:
   James C_E_T_R
   (a city in North West England).

2) Northern Irish and Sheffield United midfielder:
   Oliver N_R_O_D
   (a south London suburb).

3) Northern Irish striker:
   Conor W_S_I_G_O_
   (the capital city of the USA).

4) Played in 1996 Euros, now England manager:
   Gareth S_U_H_A_E
   (a north London suburb).

5) England striker, 1996, played for Spurs and Man Utd:
Teddy S_E_I_N_H_M
(a Norfolk seaside town).

6) England winger from 1988:
John B_R_E_
(posh south-west London riverside district).

7) Italian winger from 1988:
Fernando di N_P_L_
(a major Italian city in its native language).

8) Scottish right-back from 1980, and later a manager:
George B_R_E_
(a village in the New Forest).

9) England utility player and Liverpool star:
Gareth B_R_Y
(a Welsh seaside resort near Cardiff).

KEEPERS

Difficulty rating: Hard ⚽ ⚽ ⚽

Some of the world's best goalies were involved in the Last 16 in 2016. It's time to identify a few.

1) Thibaut Courtois was Belgium's No. 1, but who was his back-up?
   (Clue: initials SM; club: Liverpool)

2) France's goalie Hugo Lloris was also the team captain. True or false?

3) Which 'FF' was England's reserve keeper?
   (Clue: played for Southampton)

4) Wales's keeper also played for Crystal Palace: W_Y_E / H_N_E_S_Y.

5) This Arsenal stopper was Germany's back-up keeper in 2016.

6) Wojciech Szczęsny played in goal for which country?

7) Spain's Iker Casillas played for which club in 2016?

   a) Porto b) Benfica c) Sporting Lisbon

8) Italy's Gianluigi Buffon was how old in 2016?

   a) 36 b) 37 c) 38

9) Hungary's Gábor Király was forty years old during Euro 2016. True or false?

10) The Republic of Ireland's Keiren Westwood played for 'FISHY WADDLE DEFENSE' in England. Unscramble this anagram.

TEAM NICKNAMES

Difficulty rating: Hard ⚽ ⚽ ⚽

Most national teams have a nickname. Can you guess the nicknames of some of the teams who have made the Last 16 over the years?

1) *Mon dieu!* They regularly make the Last 16 and have won the Euros twice. Also known as Les Bleus (the Blues).

2) This country is an anagram of LIZARD NEWTS: known as Nati Suisse.

3) 'Norn Iron'. The only place the Republic of Ireland shares a border with.

4) Capital city Warsaw, the answer is an anagram of LAPOND: known as The White and Red.

5) This country's capital is Budapest: The Mighty Magyars.

6) One of the Last 16 teams in the 1996 tournament,
   they are England's Auld Enemy:
   The Tartan Army.

7) They come from the Emerald Isle, so their nickname
   is a perfect fit:
   The Boys in Green.

8) Their greatest-ever player is Gheorghe Hagi:
   The Tricolours.

9) You eat this at Christmas:
   The Crescent-Stars.

10) This little country between France and the Netherlands
    is one of the world's best footballing nations:
    The Red Devils.

LAST 16 – TRUE OR FALSE

Difficulty rating: Hard ⚽ ⚽ ⚽

Here are ten statements about the Euro 2016's Last 16.
Can you work out the fact from the fiction?

1) Northern Ireland's manager was Michael O'Neill.

2) Iceland had two managers.

3) And so did Slovakia.

4) Wales had just three Wales-based players in their squad.

5) Northern Ireland's Kyle Lafferty was not signed to a club during the 2016 Euros.

6) Belgium had more Premier League players in its squad than Wales.

7) Bastian Schweinsteiger was Germany's captain.

8) Slovakia had just one Premier League player.

9) Portugal's extra-time winner over Croatia was the game's first shot on target.

10) Wayne Rooney became England's most-capped player in the 2–1 loss to Iceland.

A-Z OF THE LAST 16

Difficulty rating: Medium ⚽ ⚽

Twenty-six questions about the Last 16 in 2016, and twenty-six answers required.

A – Morata. Spain forward.

B – Robert Lewandowski's club.

C – Capital of Wales.

D – Eric. Spurs. England.

E – Ross Barkley's team in 2016.

F – Bruno Alves's club in Turkey.

G – Will G_ _ _ _. He's on fire!

H – Home country of Rubik's Cube inventor.

I – Northern, or Republic of.

J – Moutinho. Portugal. Pronounced 'zho-wow'.

K – Spanish midfielder: K_K_.

L – Podolski. Germany forward.

M – Shkodran. Germany defender.

N – Radja N_I_G_O_A_. Belgian midfielder.

O – O_I_I_R Giroud. France.

P – France's biggest club.

Q – London club of Conor Washington.

R – Lukaku.

S – Shane Long's UK club. The Saints.

T – Spain midfielder. Anagram: 'I A GOTH'.

U – Emil Hallfreðsson's Italian club.

V – Behrami. Switzerland and West Ham.

W – Axel W_T_E_. Belgian midfielder.

X – Spanish midfield maestro.

Y – Carrasco. Belgian forward.

Z – Croatia's capital city.

SECTION 4

THE LAST 8 TO THE FINAL

GUV'NORS!

Difficulty rating: Hard ⚽ ⚽ ⚽

This one's all about team managers. Which one are you – a Klopp or a flop?

1) After coaching Italy to the 2016 quarter-finals, A_T_N_O / C_N_E landed the Chelsea job.

2) This Spain coach's name literally translates into English as 'Vincent from the Woods'. His team beat Portugal in the 2012 semi-finals (and won the final).

3) Russia's quarter-final coach from 2008 was from the Netherlands and also managed Chelsea and Manchester United. Clue: his initials are 'GH'.

4) The coach for an England squad who lost in the 2012 quarter-final, and who took over at Crystal Palace in 2017.

5) Berti Vogts – Germany's coach for Euro 1992, when they reached the semi-final – later managed Scotland. True or false?

6) He took Germany to the 2016 semis and his last name is pronounced 'Love'.

7) England's 1996 coach also managed Barcelona, where he was called 'El Tel'.

8) The coach for the 2016 Netherlands team who reached the quarter-finals, was their former star striker. Unscramble 'SCAB OVER MANTRA' to identify him.

9) Laurent Blanc led France to the 2012 quarter finals. True or false?

10) England's Swedish-born coach in 2004, when they reached the quarter-finals, had the initials SGE.

ENGLAND'S SEMI-FINAL STORY - 1968

Difficulty rating: Hard ⚽ ⚽ ⚽

England first made the Euro semis in 1968. Although that's about a thousand years ago, see if you can answer any of these! Take a guess if you don't know!

1) How many of England's World Cup-winning team from 1966 also played in the Euro '68 semi?

a) Three   b) Five   c) Seven

2) Pick out the 1968 players from this 1966 World Cup team:

a) Gordon Banks   b) George Cohen
c) Jack Charlton   d) Bobby Moore
e) Ray Wilson   f) Nobby Stiles
g) Alan Ball   h) Bobby Charlton
i) Martin Peters   j) Geoff Hurst
k) Roger Hunt

3) Who did England play in the semis?

a) Czechoslovakia   b) Yugoslavia   c) West Germany

4) Which England player was sent off during that game (number clue: 1-12-1-14 / 13-21-12-12-5-18-25)?

5) England's manager was: S_ R / A_ F / R_ _ _ _ Y

6) England lost the semi-final, but by what score?

a) 1–0   b) 2–0   c) 2–1

7) England did, however, win the third-place play-off – against who?

a) USSR   b) France   c) Scotland

BEHIND EVERY MAN...

Difficulty rating: Medium ⚽ ⚽

Can you identify these Euro stars, past and present, from their partners who have supported them every step of the way? We have given you each player's initials in brackets to help you, as well as the Euro championships they first appeared in.

1) He had just married Posh Spice Victoria Adams back then. Today, she's a successful fashion designer (DB, 2000).

2) Cheryl Tweedy was in Girls Aloud when she met this Arsenal and England left-back (AC, 2004).

3) This tricky French winger converted to Islam after marrying French-Algerian Wahiba Belhami (FR, 2008).

4) Real Madrid's goalkeeper married Eva González, a Spanish actress and TV presenter (IC, 2008).

5) This Netherlands forward, who played for Spurs, married Sylvie Meis live on Dutch TV (RvdV, 2008).

6) A Barcelona legend, this defender's wife is pop superstar Shakira (GP, 2008).

7) Former *The One Show* presenter Christine Bleakley is this England midfielder's wife (FL, 2012).

8) Irina Shayk is the on-off partner of this Portuguese Galactico (CR, 2012).

9) A Belgium and Manchester City midfield genius, he proposed to Michèle Lacroix under the Eiffel Tower (KDB, 2016).

WALES AT THE SEMIS!

Difficulty rating: Hard ⚽ ⚽ ⚽

Wales reached the semis in 2016. Let's celebrate that achievement with some tricky questions!

1) Who was Wales's captain at the 2016 Euros?

2) Name the only Wales team member who was playing outside the UK in 2016
   (Clue: he's a super-famous Galáctico megastar!).

3) Aaron Ramsey was with Arsenal in 2016. Who did he sign for in 2019?

4) The two Reading players in the 2016 Wales squad were: Chris G_N_E_ and Hal R_B_O_ / K_N_.

5) Who did Wales beat in the quarter-finals?

   a) Italy   b) Germany   c) Belgium

6) And by what score?

   a) 2–0　　　　　 b) 2–1　　　　　 c) 3–1

7) Who did Wales lose to in the semis?

   a) Portugal　　　 b) Spain　　　　 c) Czech Republic

8) By what score?

   a) 2–0　　　　　 b) 2–1　　　　　 c) 3–0

9) The goal scorers in that semi-final were 'ORLANDO' and 'INAN'. Who were they? Unscramble the anagrams to find out.

10) Who was Wales's manager?

   a) Mark Hughes　　 b) Chris Coleman　　 c) Ryan Giggs

PENALTY SHOOT-OUTS

Difficulty rating: Medium ⚽ ⚽

Penalties and penalty shoot-outs have decided the Euro quarter- and semi-finals on more than a few occasions. How many can you score here?

1) England has a TERRIBLE record in shoot-outs – but who did they beat in the 1996 quarter-finals?

   a) Spain   b) Italy   c) France

2) And who did England then lose to in the semis?

   a) Czech Republic   b) Germany   c) Netherlands

3) Who missed the crucial kick in that semi-final shoot-out, but later went on to manage England?

4) Oh dear. England lost in the penalty shoot-out of the 2004 quarter-finals. To whom?

   a) Italy   b) Denmark   c) Portugal

5) In the 2008 quarter-finals, 'KUTREY' beat 'ACTORIA' 3–1 in the shoot-out. Unscramble the country names.

6) In the 2004 quarter-final shoot-out Nederland beat Sverige 5–4. Can you translate both countries' names into English?

7) C_A_E_C_ / S_E_O_F missed for the Netherlands in their 5–4 quarter-final penalty shoot-out loss to France in 1996.

8) M_R_O / V_N / B_S_E_ also missed for the Dutch, in 1992 against Denmark in the semis.

9) Which Arsenal and Barcelona star scored the spot-kick winner in Spain's 2008 quarter-final triumph over Italy?

10) Who did France lose to in the 1996 semi-final shoot-out?

a) Czech Republic   b) Croatia   c) Poland

TEAM NICKNAMES

Difficulty rating: Medium ⚽ ⚽

Most national teams have a nickname, so see if you can guess these for Euro quarter- and semi-finalists.

1) A particularly easy one to start. The 1996 semi-finalists:
    Three Lions

2) Surprise semi-finalists in 2016 from the UK:
    The Dragons

3) Hola! Most successful team of recent years. Reached the semis in 2012:
    La Roja (The Red One)

4) Semi-finals in 2004 (and they won the final too!):
    Sky blue and whites

5) Most successful Euro team ever? Semi-finalists in 1996 and many other occasions:
    DFB Eleven

6) Quarter-finals in 1996. Nickname describes their kit design: the Checks

7) Semi-finalists in 2000:
Gli Azzurri (the Blues)

8) Very surprising quarter-finalists in 2016 from a volcanic island:
Our Boys

9) Semi-finalists (and winners) in 1988. Name says it all:
Oranje (Orange)

10) Semis in 2004. And they won the whole championship in 2016:
Team of Shields

ENGLAND'S SEMI-FINAL STORY - 1996

Difficulty rating: Medium ⚽ ⚽

England came oh-so-close to reaching the final in 1996, but fell just a little bit short. These questions explore both their hope and their disappointment.

1) Okay, let's get this out of the way. Who did England lose to in their semi-final?

   a) Germany   b) Germany   c) Germany

2) What was the score of that semi-final at full-time?

   a) 1–1   b) 2–2   c) 3–3

3) Who with the initials A.S. scored for England?

4) Paul 'Gazza' Gascoigne was England's star player. Which club was he playing for during 1996?

   a) Spurs   b) Lazio   c) Glasgow Rangers

5) Who was England's captain?

   a) Stuart Pearce   b) Tony Adams   c) David Platt

6) Which England player nearly won it at the end but struck
   the post?
   (An anagram of his name is 'END ON RADAR RENT',
   while his initials are 'DA'.)

7) What was the score in the penalty shoot-out?

   a) 5–4   b) 6–5   c) 7–6

8) Andreas M_L_E_ scored the winning penalty for Germany.

9) The game took place in which English stadium?

IT'S ALL GREEK!

Difficulty rating: Hard ⚽ ⚽ ⚽

The Greece national team reached the Euro semi-finals in 2004. Several of its squad's players' first or second names can be translated into English, so that's what we've done here. See if you can translate them back to Greek! This a super-tricky one, so well done if you know any of these.

1) Striker capped eighty-eight times by Greece:
   Angel Nice (A_G_L_S / C_A_I_T_A_)

2) Defensive midfielder who enjoyed a short spell at Portsmouth:
   Angel King (A_G_L_S / B_S_N_S)

3) Hard-working striker:
   Living Vyrzas (Z_S_S / V_Y_A_)

4) Central defender who played for Bordeaux,
Olympiakos and AEK Athens:
Michael Burn (M_C_A_L_S / K_P_I_)

5) Reserve goalkeeper:
Constantine Copper (K_N_T_N_I_O_ / C_A_K_A_)

6) Attacking midfielder with a great free kick in his locker:
Basil Tassel (V_S_I_I_S / T_I_R_A_)

7) Defensive midfielder, also known to play in goal
when needed:
Completely Coffee (P_N_E_I_ / K_F_S)

8) Speedy winger nicknamed 'Turbo' who enjoyed a
season with Crystal Palace in 2004/05:
Basil Lacquer (V_S_L_S / L_K_S)

STAT ATTACK

Difficulty rating: Medium ✪ ✪

The Euros have thrown up some great facts and figures for lovers of statistics, especially the quarter-finals and semis.

1) Which team has had the most top-eight finishes in Euro history?

   a) Spain
   b) Italy
   c) West Germany/Germany

2) The Italy 0–0 Netherlands semi in 2000 is infamous for what reason?

   a) No shots on target
   b) The Euros' dirtiest game
   c) Match abandoned due to floodlight failure

3) In 1960, France and Yugoslavia fought out the highest-scoring semi-final yet. What was the score?

   a) 3–4   b) 4–4   c) 4–5

4) In the 1976 semi against Yugoslavia, West Germany's Dieter Müller made history when he came off the bench and on to the pitch. What happened next?

a) He scored a hat-trick
b) He was sent off
c) He was substituted ten minutes later

5) Which team has the most top-eight finishes without winning the Euros?

a) Turkey
b) England
c) Czechoslovakia/Czech Republic

6) In the 2012 England v Italy quarter-final, Italy managed thirty-five goal attempts. How many did England have?

a) 9   b) 25   c) 41

THE A–Z OF THE QUARTER- AND SEMI-FINALS

Difficulty rating: Medium 🌐 🌐

Twenty-six questions about the last eight and last four from all of Euro history; twenty-six answers required.

A – Andrey. Russia and Arsenal, 2008.

B – Gareth. Plays for Wales.

C – Country. Now called Czech Republic.

D – Edgar. Netherlands, 2000.

E – E_R_ Belözoğlu. Turkey, 2008.

F – Lampard's first name.

G – Country. Capital: Athens.

H – 'Greece' in Greek: 'SHEALL' (anagram).

I – Ciro. Italy defender, 2016.

J – Carragher. England.

K – Dutch. Patrick. 'VERTIKUL' (anag.).

L – France 1990s goalie. Bernard 'AMAL'(anagram).

M – Belgium. Fellaini's first name.

N – Lost 1992 semis. AKA Holland.

O – Divock. Liverpool forward.

P – José Fonte's country.

Q – Portugal goalie, 2004: Q_ _ M.

R – R_M_N_A. Country. Last eight, 2000.

S – S_ M Vokes. Wales striker

T – Fernando. Spain. Top scorer 2012.

U – Ismael U_ _ _ _ Z. Spain 2000.

V – David. Top scorer 2008.

W – Country. Locals call it Cymru.

X – Abel X_V_E_. Portugal, 2000.

Y – Lev. Russia. Best goalie ever. 1950s-70s.

Z – Spain goalie, 1996.

FINAL SCORES

Difficulty rating: Easy

A nice easy one for you – a quick trot through some of the past Euro Championships Finals. What were the scores?

1)   1960. USSR v Yugoslavia.

    a) 2–1   b) 1–2   c) 3–0

2)   1968. Italy v Yugoslavia.

    a) 2–1   b) 2–0   c) 4–2

3)   1972. West Germany v USSR.

    a) 1–0   b) 2–0   c) 3–0

4)   1984. France v Spain.

    a) 1–0   b) 2–0   c) 3–0

5)   1988. USSR v Netherlands.

    a) 1–0   b) 0–2   c) 1–3

6) 1996. Czech Republic v Germany.

    a) 1–2   b) 1–3   c) 2–3

7) 2000. France v Italy.

    a) 2–1   b) 3–1   c) 0–2

8) 2008. Germany v Spain.

    a) 0–1   b) 1–0   c) 2–0

9) 2012. Spain v Italy.

    a) 2–0   b) 3–0   c) 4–0

10) 2016. Portugal v Spain.

    a) 1–0   b) 0–1   c) 2–1

EXTRA TIME AND GOLDEN GOALS

Difficulty rating: Hard ⚽ ⚽ ⚽

There's nothing better than an extra-time winner in a big final – except maybe a golden goal. And the Euros have had their fair share of both.

1) The 1976 final went to extra time. What was the score at full time?

   a) 0–0   b) 1–1   c) 2–2

2) The teams were Czechoslovakia (now the Czech Republic) and West Germany. Who won in extra time?

3) Who scored Portugal's extra-time winner in 2016?

   a) Eder   b) Edam   c) Edna

4) The first final, in 1960, was also the first to go to extra time. True or false?

5) What was the score in that game at full time?

   a) 1–1   b) 2–2   c) 3–3

6) Valentin Bubukin scored the extra-time winner.
   True or false?

7) The 1996 final was won with a golden goal in extra time.
   Who did Germany beat?

8) The winning goal scorer's name when translated literally
   into English is 'Oliver Beer House'. What is it in German?

9) Italy led the 2000 final 1–0 until extra time.
   Who equalized for France?
   (Clue: S_L_A_N / W_L_O_D).

10) David Trezeguet, France's golden goal scorer in that same
    final, played for which Italian club in Turin?

HOT SHOTS

Difficulty rating: Hard ⚽ ⚽ ⚽

Apart from scoring the winning goal in the final, every striker wants to be the tournament's top scorer. Like these guys!

1) The joint top scorers in the first Euros in 1960 each scored how many goals?

   a) Two   b) Four   c) Six

2) Geoff Hurst and Bobby Charlton were top scorers for England in 1968 with how many goals?

3) Which German with the surname Müller was the top scorer in 1972?

   a) Horst   b) Dieter   c) Gerd

4) And which German with the surname Müller was the top scorer in 1976?

   a) Horst   b) Dieter   c) Gerd

5) 'CLAIM IN THE LIP' is an anagram of the name of which Frenchman, who bagged a record-breaking nine goals in 1984?

6) Who was top scorer in 1992: Henrik Larsen (Denmark) or Henrik Larsson (Sweden)?

7) Which Englishman topped the goal-scoring table on home soil in 1996?

8) Savo Milošević and Patrick Kluivert both scored five goals in 2000, but for which respective teams?

9) Wayne Rooney was the top scorer of 2004. True or false?

10) Which Frenchman scored six in 2016, and then signed for Barcelona in 2019?

CAPTAINS FANTASTIC!

Difficulty rating: Medium ⚽ ⚽

Okay – your mission here is to identify these Euro-winning captains. How many will you get?

1) 1964. Spain

    a) Feliciano Rivilla   b) Amancio Amaro
    c) Ferran Olivella

2) 1968. Italy

    a) Aristide Guarneri   b) Giacinto Facchetti
    c) Giorgio Ferrini

3) 1972. West Germany

    a) Franz Beckenbauer   b) Paul Breitner
    c) Herbert Wimmer

4) 1988. The Netherlands

    a) Ronald Koeman   b) Ruud Gullit   c) Marco van Basten

5) 1992. Denmark

   a) Peter Schmeichel   b) Lars Olsen   c) John Jensen

6) 1996. Germany

   a) Matthias Sammer   b) Thomas Helmer
   c) Jürgen Klinsmann

7) 2000. France

   a) Didier Deschamps   b) Zinedine Zidane
   c) Marcel Desailly

8) 2008. Spain

   a) Iker Casillas   b) Sergio Ramos   c) Xavi

9) 2012. Spain

   a) Iker Casillas   b) Sergio Ramos   c) Xavi

10) 2016. Portugal

   a) Pepe   b) José Fonte   c) Cristiano Ronaldo

PENALTIES, 1976 STYLE

Difficulty rating: Hard ⚽ ⚽ ⚽

To date, the 1976 Euro final has been the only one to be decided by penalties. Have a go at answering these questions all about that final.

1) Both teams in the final contained only home-based players. True or false?

2) What was the score at full time?

   a) 2–2   b) 3–3   c) 4–4

3) The Czechs squandered their early lead of 2–0. True or false?

4) The German teàm contained two future national managers: B_R_I_/ V_G_S and F_A_Z / B_C_E_B_U_R.

5) The German keeper Sepp Maier was the first person to wear outsize 'Mickey Mouse' gloves. True or false?

6) Czech defender Jozef Čapkovič had a twin brother, also a professional footballer. True or false?

7) The final was played in Belgrade, located in which modern-day country?

   a) Serbia   b) Bosnia   c) Croatia

8) How many consecutive penalties were converted in the shoot-out?

   a) Five   b) Six   c) Seven

9) Who took the winning penalty?

   a)   Koloman Gögh
   b)   Antonín Panenka
   c)   Ján Pivarník

10) What was the final penalty score?

   a) 4–3   b) 5–3   c) 6–5

STADIUM ROCKS!

Difficulty rating: Easy 🌐

The Euro Championship finals have been played in some of the world's greatest arenas. Test your knowledge here!

1) Italy's Stadio Olimpico is one of only two venues to host the final twice. In which city is it?

2) France's Parc des Princes is the other venue, but where is it?

3) The 2020 final will be held in which iconic stadium for the second time in the history of the Euros?

4) The 2004 final was held in Portugal's Estádio da Luz. How does that translate into English?

5) Munich's Olympiastadion held the 1988 final. Which two German club sides played their home games there until 2006?

6) Which final-hosting stadium has the largest capacity?

   a) Parc des Princes   b) Olympiastadion   c) Wembley

7) Ullevi, home of the 1992 final, is in which city?

   a) Gothenburg   b) Malmö   c) Stockholm

8) And in which country?

9) Which Spanish La Liga team plays its home games at the Santiago Bernabéu Stadium, where the 1964 final was played?

10) The 2000 final was held in the Stadion Feijenoord in the Netherlands. In which city?

   a) Rotterdam   b) The Hague   c) Amsterdam

THE FINALS IN NUMBERS

Difficulty rating: Hard ⚽ ⚽ ⚽

At the end of every Euro tournament, the numbers, stats, facts and figures are usually mind-boggling. So, boggle your mind for some of these.

1) Almost 2.5 million people attended the 2016 Euros.
   True or false?

2) The 1974 Team of the Tournament saw a record number of players from one country selected. How many?

3) And from which country?

   a) Italy   b) Netherlands   c) West Germany

4) Fewer than 80,000 people attended the first-ever Euros in 1960.
   True or false?

5) Which country has supplied the most players for the Team of the Tournament?

   a) West Germany / Germany   b) Spain   c) France

6) How many England players have made the Team of the Tournament?

   a) Five   b) Seven   c) Nine

7) The highest average attendance was in 1988. How many?

   a) 41,773   b) 59,243   c) 67,551

8) Which team has scored the most goals across all Euro tournaments?

   a) France   b) Portugal   c) Germany

9) Which team has let in the most goals across all Euro tournaments?

   a) Germany   b) Russia   c) Yugoslavia

10) Which nation's team has drawn the most across all the Euro championships?

   a) Portugal   b) Scotland   c) Italy

TEAMS OF THE TOURNAMENT

Difficulty rating: Medium ⚽ ⚽

It's a special honour to be selected for the Team of the Tournament (ToT) at the end of every European Championship. See if you know who made the cut.

1) Name the only two Welsh players to have made the ToT in 2016. Their initials are JA and AR.

2) Three goalies have been in the ToT twice. They are…

   a) L_V / Y_S_I_ (USSR/Russia)
   b) D_N_ / Z_F_ (Italy)
   c) I_E_ / C_S_L_A_

3) Luis Suárez was once named in the Euro ToT. True or false?

4) Which pair of England 1966 World Cup winners got into the 1968 Euro ToT?

5) And which London club did they both play for?

6) Czechoslovakia's Antonín Panenka made the 1976 ToT. What, today, is a 'Panenka'?

7) Which elegant Italian defender and AC Milan star is the only three-time member of the ToT club, in 1988, 1996 and 2000?

8) Who were Alan and Paul, the two Geordies in the 1996 ToT?

9) Spain's Xavi earned his ToT place in 2008 and 2012. What is his full name?

10) In 2008, Hamit Altıntop became the only player to date from which country to make the ToT?

STAT ATTACK: THE FINALS!

Difficulty rating: Medium ⚽ ⚽

The Euro finals have thrown up some amazing facts and figures – and here are a few to think about!

1) The highest final attendance was 79,115 in 1964. Which famous Spanish stadium hosted?

   a) Bernabéu, Madrid
   b) Camp Nou, Barcelona
   c) Mestalla, Valencia

2) The lowest attendance at a final was in 1960. How many?

   a) 18,000   b) 25,000   c) 31,000

3) Spain and Germany have the most wins in the final. How many?

4) The oldest player to appear in a final was aged thirty-eight years and 232 days.
   True or false?

5) The fastest-ever goal in a final came after how
   many minutes?

   a) Six minutes
   b) Eight minutes
   c) Nine minutes

6) Germany and the USSR have the most losses in the final.
   How many?

7) France v Italy in 2000 was the first final decided by a
   'Golden Goal'.
   True or false?

8) Fourteen nations have appeared in the Euro finals.
   How many no longer exist?

9) Renato Sanches was the youngest player to appear in a
   final, at eighteen years 328 days. For which country?

10) Only one player has ever been sent off in a final.
    True or false?

THE A–Z OF THE FINALS

Difficulty rating: Medium ⚽ ⚽

From A–Z, here is everything you need to know about the
European Championship finals past and present!

A – Country. 2008:
A_S_R_A

B – Laudrup.
Danish winner, 1992

C – First name of Fàbregas

D – Trezeguet.
France player, 2000

E – Country. 1996:
E_G_A_D

F – Stade de F_ _ _ _ _.
2016 final

G – Country. 2004 winners:
G_E_C_

H – Belgian stadium.
1972 final

I – Netto.
USSR captain, 1960

J – Klinsmann.
Germany, 1996

K – Viktor K_L_T_V.
USSR. 1972

L – City. Portugal.
2004 final

M – Clattenburg.
Referee, 2016

N – N_N_.
Portugal. 2016.
Ex-Man U

O – Anton. Czech. 1976.
'ROUNDS' (anagram)

P – Vieira. France. 2000

Q – Ricardo Q_A_E_M_.
Portugal sub 2016

R – Sergio.
Spain defender. 2012

S – USSR was also called
S_V_E_ / U_I_N

T – Jean. France, 1984.
'A GIANT' (anagram)

U – Dušan U_R_N.
Czech manager, 1996

V – Austrian capital.
2008 final

W – W_S_ Germany.
Winners '72 and '80

X – Alonso. Spain.
2012 winner

Y – Former country. Lost
1960 final

Z – Dino.
Italy manager, 2000

SECTION 5

THE ANSWERS

ANSWERS

Quiz 1

1) A, of course!

2) The correct combinations are:

Czech Republic	Prague
Bulgaria	Sofia
Montenegro	Podgorica
Kosovo	Prishtina

3) Harry Kane: 4–0 Bulgaria and 7–0 Montenegro.

4) Czech Republic: 2–1 away

5) Three: Kane, McGuire and Winks

6) Keiran Trippier (Atlético Madrid) and Jadon Sancho (Borussia Dortmund)

7) Mason Mount

8) Chelsea. Surprising, eh?

9)

Fikayo Tomori	Ross Barkley
Ruben Loftus-Cheek	Mason Mount
Tammy Abraham	Callum Hudson-Odoi

10) St Mary's Stadium, Southampton, in the 5–3 win over Kosovo

11) Trent Alexander-Arnold

12) Harry Kane – again!

Quiz 2

1) Norway

2) Patrick Kluivert

3) Bobby Moore

4) Slovakia

5) Cesc Fabregas

6) George Best

7) True, though Wales lost 5–1 to Slovakia

8) Romelu Lukaku

9) Cruyff

10) Kylian Mbappé

Quiz 3

1) Cristiano Ronaldo. Who else?

2) 31 (including 11 for the 2020 campaign!)

3) David Healey (2008 qualifying), Robert Lewandowski (2016 qualifying)

4) Luxembourg

5) Malcolm MacDonald and Marco van Basten

6) Germany

7) Gianluigi Buffon

8) Dino Zoff

9) Germany. Always Germany!

10) Seven, from 1992–2020

Quiz 4

1) B. The Golfer
2) RB Leipzig (on loan from Chelsea)
3) Four wins, two draws and two losses
4) Cardiff City Stadium
5) Aaron Ramsey
6) Azerbaijan
7) Wayne Hennessey
8) C. 672
9) Luka Modrić
10) B. twice – 2016 and 2020

Quiz 5

1) Eric Dier
2) Ross Barkley
3) Aaron Wan-Bissaka
4) Raheem Sterling
5) Dele Alli
6) Declan Rice
7) Jesse Lingard
8) Joe Gomez
9) Kieran Trippier
10) Harry Winks
11) Ben Chilwell
12) Tammy Abraham

Quiz 6

1) Wales
2) Israel
3) Andorra
4) Greece
5) Turkey
6) Montenegro
7) Switzerland
8) Liechtenstein
9) Republic of Ireland
10) Sweden

Quiz 7

1) All three

2) Four

3) C. 5,220,354 – an average of 36.5 per country!

4) Raheem Sterling (6)

5) A. 19

6) A. 51 per cent

7) B. 3.2

8) C. San Marino

9) One scored; 51 conceded

10) A. Every 28.1 minutes, to be exact

Quiz 8

1) 55

2) 250

3) 801

4) 43

5) Spain. 91 per cent!

6) Spain again. 70 per cent!!

7) Er… Spain, with 227 shots!!!

8) Gotcha! It was Belgium, with 40 goals

9) Harry Kane – 12

10) Henry Bonello made 49 saves

Quiz 9

SCOTLAND

1 David Marshall
2 Stephen O'Donnell
3 Andy Robertson
4 Charlie Mulgrew
5 Liam Cooper
6 Scott McTominay

10 Callum McGregor
16 Kenny McLean
17 Robert Snodgrass
19 Matthew Phillips
20 Ryan Christie

Quiz 9

BELGIUM

1 Thibaut Courtois
2 Toby Alderweireld
3 Thomas Vermaelen
5 Jan Vertonghen
6 Leander Dendoncker
7 Kevin de Bruyne

8 Youri Tielemans
9 Romelu Lukaku
14 Dries Mertens
15 Thomas Meunier
22 Nacer Chadli

Quiz 10

Albania	Jadon	Szczęsny
Blind	Kompany	Tallinn
Cristiano	Lasagna	Umtiti
Deutschland	Moutinho	Volksparkstadion
Eriksen	Novgorod	Wijnaldum
Fabianski	Origi	Xhaka
Giorgio	Polska	Yuri
Hampden Park	Qualifiers	Zola
Iceland	Ronald	

Quiz 11

1) Wayne Rooney

2) C. Boro!

3) B. 2 minutes

4) C. Incredible but true

5) France

6) B. Germany

7) Lothar Matthäus

8) Rafael Gordillo

9) False – it was Dirk Kuyt!

10) A. 15 minutes

Quiz 12

1) A. Zidane
2) C. Switzerland
3) Andrea Pirlo
4) Sweden
5) Alan Shearer
6) A. Turkey
7) McAllister
8) A. (It was what the USSR became)
9) Filippo Inzaghi

Quiz 13

1) A. 25
2) Bulgaria and Spain (1-1)
3) Bastian Schweinsteiger
4) 2000 and 2004. Six each
5) No reds from 1960 to 1980
6) Greece and Poland (1-1)
7) C. After 24 minutes!
8) Just under 50 per cent: 12 of 25
9) A. 10 out of 25 reds were issued in the final 10 minutes
10) France, in the 1–0 victory over Denmark in 1984
11) Keith Andrews, in the 2012 loss to Italy
12) None (so far!)

Quiz 14

1) Zlatan!
2) Zlatan!!
3) Paul Gascoigne
4) Luis Figo
5) Ray Wilkins
6) Zinedine Zidane
7) Zlatan!!!
8) Henrik Larsson
9) Whelan
10) Tomas Brolin

Quiz 15

1) Didier Deschamps
2) Dennis Bergkamp
3) Emmanuel Petit
4) Pep Guardiola
5) Luis Figo
6) Frank Leboeuf
7) Johann Vogel
8) Enrico Chiesa
9) Raul Bravo
10) Laurent Blanc
11) Fabio Grosso
12) Dimitris Salpingidis

Quiz 16

1) Michel Platini
2) Michel Platini
3) Michel Platini, in the 1984 Yugoslavia game
4) Michel Platini
5) Michel Platini
6) Michel Platini... sorry, I mean true!
7) Spain
8) England
9) Portugal
10) West Germany
11) A. Six
12) A. None!

Quiz 17

1) True
2) True
3) False. It was Slovenia's Srečko Katanec in 2000, aged 36.
4) True
5) False – it was after 67 seconds!
6) False. He was 38.
7) True – against Portugal.
8) False. He is Dutch.
9) False – Portugal does (7, from 1984–2016

126

Quiz 18

1) A. 18

2) A. Portugal – 4 goals

3) A. 3

4) C. Zidane. In the 2004 win over England

5) B. Ronaldo!

6) Euros 2004

7) False. There were zero injury time goals in 2016!

8) Wayne Rooney

9) B. 96th

10) Dimitri Payet and Niall McGinn

Quiz 19

1) Albania

2) Norway

3) Ukraine

4) Bulgaria

5) Austria

6) Slovenia

7) Latvia

8) Scotland

Quiz 20

A – Alessandro

B – Berlin

C – Claude

D – Dennis

E – Edwin

F – Fernando Llorente

G – Galatasaray

H – Hummels

I – Illgner

J – Joleon

K – Karim

L – Lyon

M – Manchester United

N – Neville Neville

O – Oxlade

P – Papastathopoulos

Q – Quinn

R – Roberto

S – Sweden

T – Tomas

U – UEFA

V – Valencia

W – Walcott

X – Xhaka

Y – Youri

Z – Zenden

Quiz 21

1) Belgium
2) Italy
3) Portugal
4) Switzerland
5) France
6) Germany
7) Spain
8) Iceland
9) Wales
10) Croatia
11) Slovakia
12) Hungary
13) Poland
14) Northern Ireland
15) Republic of Ireland
16) England

Quiz 22

1) Yann Sommer
2) Toni Kroos
3) Ciro Immobile
4) Ricardo Carvalho
5) Lucas Digne
6) Manuel Neuer
7) Graziano Pelle
8) Raphaël Guerreiro
9) Luka Modrić
10) Lorenzo Insigne
11) Petr Čech
12) Fabian Frei

Quiz 23

1) Ivan Rakitic
2) Birkir Bjarnason
3) Eliaquim Mangala
4) Bartosz Salamon
5) Breel Embolo
6) Mario Mandzukic
7) Vieirinha
8) Andrea Barzagli
9) Bacary Sagna
10) Marek Hamsik
11) Aritz Aduriz
12) Marc-André ter Stegen

Quiz 24

1) Germany	5) Belgium	9) Croatia
2) Italy	6) Switzerland	10) Iceland
3) Portugal	7) England	
4) Spain	8) Wales	

Quiz 25

1) True – 12 each

2) a.) Hugo Lloris   b.) Kyle Walker
   c.) Danny Rose   d.) Harry Kane
   e.) Eric Dier   f.) Dele Alli
   g.) Ben Davies   h.) Toby Alderweireld
   i.) Jan Vertonghen j.) Mousa Dembélé

3) a.) Anthony Martial   b.) Morgan Schneiderlin
   c.) Chris Smalling   d.) Wayne Rooney
   e.) Marcus Rashford   f.) Bastian Schweinsteiger
   g.) Paddy McNair   h.) David de Gea
   i.) Marouane Fellaini   j.) Matteo Darmian

4) Robbie Keane

Quiz 26

1) Chester	4) Southgate	7) Naples (Napoli)
2) Norwood	5) Sheringham	8) Burley
3) Washington	6) Barnes	9) Barry

Quiz 27

1) Simon Mignolet
2) True
3) Fraser Forster
4) Wayne Hennessey
5) Bernd Leno

6) Poland
7) A. Porto
8) C. 38!
9) True
10) Sheffield Wednesday

Quiz 28

1) France
2) Switzerland
3) Northern Ireland
4) Poland
5) Hungary

6) Scotland
7) Republic of Ireland
8) Romania
9) Turkey
10) Belgium

Quiz 29

1) True.
2) True – Heimir Hallgrímsson and Lars Lagerbäck.
3) False. Just Ján Kozák.
4) False. It was only two: Neil Taylor and Ashley Williams (both Swansea).
5) False. He was with Birmingham City.

6) False. They both had 11.
7) True.
8) True. Martin Škrtel of Liverpool.
9) False. It was the second!
10) True. 115 caps, along with David Beckham.

Quiz 30

A – Alvaro.
B – Bayern Munich
C – Cardiff
D – Dier
E – Everton
F – Fenerbahçe
G – Grigg
H – Hungary

I – Ireland
J – Joao
K – Koke
L – Lukas
M – Mustafi
N – Nainggolan
O – Olivier
P – PSG
Q – QPR

R – Romelu
S – Southampton
T – Thiago
U – Udinese
V – Valon
W – Witsel
X – Xavi
Y – Yannick
Z – Zagreb

Quiz 31

1) Antonio Conte
2) Vincente del Bosque
3) Guus Hiddink
4) Roy Hodgson
5) True
6) Joachim Löw
7) Terry Venables
8) Marco van Basten
9) True
10) Sven-Göran Eriksson

Quiz 32

1) C. Seven
2) Banks, Wilson, Moore, Ball, Hunt, B. Charlton, Peters
3) B. Yugoslavia
4) Alan Mullery
5) Sir Alf Ramsey
6) A. 1–0
7) A. USSR

Quiz 33

1) David Beckham

2) Ashley Cole

3) Frank Ribery

4) Iker Casillas

5) Rafael van der Vaart

6) Gerard Piqué

7) Frank Lampard

8) Cristiano Ronaldo

9) Kevin de Bruyne

Quiz 34

1) Ashley Williams

2) Gareth Bale

3) Juventus

4) Chris Gunter and
   Hal Robson-Kanu

5) C. Belgium

6) C. 3-1

7) A. Portugal

8) B. 2–0

9) Ronaldo and Nani

10) B. Chris Coleman

Quiz 35

1) A. Spain

2) B. Germany

3) Gareth Southgate

4) C. Portugal

5) Turkey, Croatia

6) Netherlands and Sweden

7) Clarence Seedorf

8) Marco van Basten

9) Cesc Fabregas

10) A. Czech Republic

Quiz 36

1) England!
2) Wales
3) Spain
4) Greece
5) Germany
6) Croatia
7) Italy
8) Iceland
9) Netherlands
10) Portugal

Quiz 37

1) Yep, Germany!
2) A. 1–1
3) Alan Shearer
4) C. Rangers
5) B. Tony Adams
6) Darren Anderton
7) B. 6–5
8) Andreas Möller
9) Wembley

Quiz 38

1) Angelos Charisteas
2) Angelos Basinas
3) Zisis Vrysas
4) Michalis Kapsis
5) Konstantinos Chalkias
6) Vassilios Tsiartas
7) Pantelis Kafes
8) Vasilis Lakis

Quiz 39

1) C. Germany – nine!
2) B. Nine yellows and one red
3) C. 4–5 to Yugoslavia
4) A. And on his debut, too!
5) B. England
6) A. 9! Game finished 0–0 (Italy won on pens)

Quiz 40

A – Arshavin
B – Bale
C – Czechoslovakia
D – (Edgar) Davids
E – Emre
F – Frank
G – Greece
H – Hellas!
I – (Ciro) Immobile
J – Jamie
K – Patrick Kluivert
L – (Bernard) Lama
M – Marouane

N – Netherlands
O – (Divock) Origi
P – Portugal
Q – Quim
R – Romania
S – Sam
T – (Fernando) Torres
U – Urzaiz
V – Villa
W – Wales
X – Xavier
Y – Yashin
Z – (Andoni) Zubizarreta

Quiz 41

1) A. 2–1 to USSR

2) B. 2–0 to Italy

3) C. 3–0 to West Germany

4) B. 2–0 to France

5) B. 0–2 to Netherlands

6) A. 1–2 to Germany

7) A. 2–1 to France

8) A. 0–1 to Spain

9) C. 4–0 to Spain

10) A. 1–0 to Portugal

Quiz 42

1) C. 2–2

2) No one! Germany won on penalties

3) A. Eder

4) True

5) A. 1–1

6) False. It was Viktor Ponedelnik

7) Czech Republic

8) Oliver Bierhoff

9) Sylvain Wiltord

10) Juventus

Quiz 43

1) A. Two.

2) One goal each!

3) C. Gerd, four goals

4) B. Dieter – no relation

5) Michel Platini

6) It was Denmark's Larsen (with two goals!)

7) Alan Shearer, five goals.

8) Yugoslavia and The Netherlands

9) False. He got four goals, Milan Baroš of the Czech Republic got five

10) Antoine Griezmann

Quiz 44

1) C. Olivella

2) B. Facchetti

3) A. Beckenbauer

4) B. Gullit

5) B. Olsen

6) C. Klinsmann

7) A. Deschamps

8) A. Casillas

9) A. Casillas

10) C. Ronaldo

Quiz 45

1) False. It was Czechoslovakia v West Germany

2) A. 2–2

3) True.

4) Bertie Vogts and Franz Beckenbauer

5) True

6) True – Jan Čapkovič

7) A. Serbia

8) C. Seven

9) B. Panenka

10) B. 5–3

Quiz 46

1) Rome

2) Paris

3) Wem-ber-lee!

4) Stadium of Light

5) Bayern Munich and TSV 1860 Munich

6) Wembley – 82,000

7) A. Gothenburg

8) Sweden

9) Real Madrid

10) A. Rotterdam

Quiz 47

1) True. The highest number so far

2) Seven

3) C. West Germany

4) True. 78,958 to be exact

5) A. West Germany / Germany (33 players)

6) A. Five (Bobby Moore and Geoff Hurst in 1968;
   Alan Shearer and Paul Gascoigne in 1996;
   Wayne Rooney in 2004)

7) B. 59,243

8) C. Germany – 72 goals scored

9) A. Germany – 48 goals conceded

10) C. Italy – 16 games drawn

Quiz 48

1) Joe Allen and Aaron Ramsey

2) A. Lev Yashin (1960, 1964)
   B. Dino Zoff (1968, 1980)
   C. Iker Casillas (2008, 2012)

3) True! It was Spain's Luis Suárez, in 1964

4) Bobby Moore and Geoff Hurst

5) West Ham United

6) A penalty where the taker cheekily chips the ball into
   the net

7) Paolo Maldini

8) Alan Shearer and Paul Gascoigne

9) Xavi Hernández

10) Turkey

Quiz 49

1) A. Bernabéu

2) A. 18,000

3) Three: Spain (1964, 2008, 2012);
Germany (1972, 1980, 1996)

4) True. For Germany in 2008

5) A. Six minutes. Jesús María Pereda, for Spain, 1964

6) Three: USSR (1964, 1972, 1988);
Germany (1976, 1992, 2008)

7) False. Czech Republic v Germany in 1996 was first

8) Four: West Germany (now part of Germany),
Czechoslovakia (now the Czech Republic),
the USSR, Yugoslavia

9) Portugal, in 2016

10) True. Yvon Le Roux, for France in 1984 against Spain

Quiz 50

A – Austria

B – Brian (Laudrup)

C – Cesc (Fàbregas)

D – David (Trezeguet)

E – England!

F – France

G – Greece

H – Heysal

I – Igor (Netto)

J – Jürgen (Klinsmann)

K – Kolotov (Viktor)

L – Lisbon

M – Mark (Clattenburg)

N – Nani

O – Ondrus (Anton)

P – Patrick (Vieira)

Q – Quaresma

R – Ramos (Sergio)

S – Soviet Union

T – Tigana (Jean)

U – Uhrin (Dušan)

V – Vienna

W – West Germany

X – Xabi (Alonso)

Y – Yugoslavia

Z – Zoff

HAVE YOU GOT THEM ALL?

ULTIMATE FOOTBALL HEROES